KEVIN & Kell
Quest for Content

Online Features Syndicate

by Bill Holbrook

http://www.reuben.org/holbrook/kevkel.html

Kevin & Kell #1 - Quest for Content is an original publication of Bill Holbrook and is published by Plan Nine Publishing.

Contents © 1997 Bill Holbrook
ISBN 1-9660676-0-6
Fourth Printing March 2002

Plan Nine
Publishing

1237 Elon Place
High Point, NC 27263
336.454.7766
www.plan9.org

*Bringing you the future tomorrow,
but what's funny today!*

Printed in the USA.

To Teri, My Wife

Acknowledgments

Thanks to David Allen without whom this book would not have been produced, and special thanks to my partner, Doug Pratt, who had an idea for marketing a comic strip in cyberpsace.

Also by Bill Holbrook & Plan Nine Publishing

Kevin & Kell
Seen Anything Unusual?
Accepting Domestication
Run Free!
For the Birds

On the Fastrack
Annual Report
Tomb Raiding for Fun & Profit

Safe Havens
The Safe Havens Annual
Dancing on the Basketball Court

6

8

9

10

11

DON'T WORRY ABOUT RUDY, KELL. MOST SONS HAVE CONFLICTS WITH THEIR STEPFATHERS.

I'M JUST GLAD HIS ARTISTIC TALENTS GIVE HIM AN EMOTIONAL OUTLET... THAT HE'S ABLE TO WORK OUT HIS FEELINGS TOWARD ME THROUGH HIS PAINTING.

SHOULDER
LOIN
RIBS
SHANK
DRUMSTICK

:AHEM: I HEREBY CHALLENGE YOU FOR THE ROLE OF THE FAMILY'S DOMINANT ALPHA MALE.

ROLL ROLL ROLL ROLL ROLL ROLL ROLL ROLL

WHAP

GO DO YOUR HOMEWORK, RUDY.

THAT **WAS** MY HOMEWORK.

13

HMM... WHAT TO WEAR... BETTER CHECK THE FORECAST.

WE PREDICT SLIGHTLY TIGHTER CLOTHES AS THE BAGGY FASHION STYLE MOVES OUT, WITH THE CAP BILL STILL WORN 180° BACKWARD... 50% CHANCE OF A CYNICAL ATTITUDE ADJUSTMENT BY MID-AFTERNOON.

"THE PEER GROUP FORUM."

TODAY'S MEANINGLESS SLANG WORD: "FREEM."

© 1995 Bill Holbrook

MOM, ARE YOU REALLY SERIOUS ABOUT KEVIN?

RUDY! I MARRIED HIM A YEAR AGO!

WE'RE DEEPLY IN LOVE! HE'S GIVEN ME A REASON TO LIVE! WHAT DID YOU THINK WHEN HE CAME TO LIVE HERE?

I DUNNO...

© 1995 Bill Holbrook

...MAYBE THAT HE WAS ONE OF THOSE "FREE-RANGE" THINGS.

15

16

18

19

20

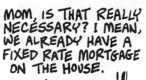

23

24

25

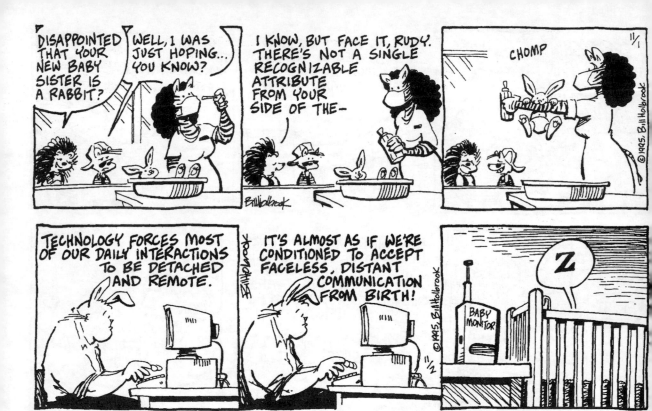

26

27

ONE WEEK AFTER GIVING BIRTH, KELL'S BOSS MAKES HER RETURN TO WORK!

...SO KEVIN STAYS HOME TENDING A BUNNY WITH THE APPETITE OF A WOLF!

SCHOOL BUS

CALIBAN ACADEMY

© 1995. Bill Holbrook

YEAH! GOOD THING HE FOUND A PLACE THAT GIVES ADVICE TO PARENTS OF CARNIVOROUS OFFSPRING!

11/7

WELCOME TO THE ANKLEBITER FORUM

REALLY, KELL? CONEY'S A BIG HIT WITH YOUR FAMILY?

YES, KEVIN! AT FIRST THEY COULDN'T ACCEPT A BUNNY AS ONE OF THEIR OWN...

...BUT AFTER A WHILE SHE WON THEM OVER!

HOW?

DIAPER BAG

SHE GOT RID OF THEIR GNOME INFESTATION.

PTOO!

DO YOU KNOW WHAT PEST CONTROL WOULD'VE CHARGED?

© 1995. Bill Holbrook

11/8

28

29

HOW CAN I LEAVE MY NEW BABY AND GO TO WORK EACH MORNING?

HOW CAN I VOICE MY ANXIETIES TO MY HUSBAND WITHOUT SEEMING TO QUESTION HIS PARENTING ABILITIES?

HOW CAN I PURSUE MY CAREER WHILE BEING SO... SO...

...PREOCCUPIED?

YEAH, I HAVEN'T HAD A KILL ALL WEEK.

WHAT'S **THAT**, KELL?

I WANTED THE WHOLE OFFICE TO SEE MY BABY, L.D.!

ISN'T SHE CUTE? SO SOFT... SO WARM... SO FLUFFY...

CAUSE OF DEATH?

DROWNED IN HIS OWN SALIVA.

31

33

34

36

37

38

39

41

42

43

44

45

47

49

51

FIONA, I...I NEVER THOUGHT I COULD FEEL THIS WAY ABOUT... ABOUT...

HEY! THE MOON'S GOING DOWN! I'M TURNING BACK INTO MY NORMAL SELF!

YOU PUT ME UNDER A SPELL! A CURSE! GET AWAY FROM ME, VILE ENCHANTRESS!

♪ SEE YOU NEXT MONTH? ♪

I'LL CALL YOU.

IT WAS BIZARRE! THE FULL MOON MADE ME MANNERED... CONSIDERATE... KIND... I WASN'T MYSELF!

GIRLS CAN DO THAT TO YOU, MAN.

BUT WHERE CAN I FIND A CURE BEFORE NEXT MONTH?

HMM... WE COULD CONSULT THE MYSTIC RUNES... THE LORE OF THE ELDERS...

...OR ACCESS THE ONLINE MALE SUPPORT GROUP!

"GO TESTOSTERONE?"

MOM... KEVIN... YOU SHOULD KNOW THAT I'VE BEEN PLACED UNDER A CURSE.

A GIRL AT SCHOOL TURNED ME INTO SOMETHING THAT BECOMES CIVILIZED UNDER A FULL MOON. THANK YOU.

MAYBE WE CAN THROW OUT THOSE BROCHURES FOR OBEDIENCE SCHOOLS!

LET'S WAIT 'TIL HE STOPS DRINKING OUT OF THE TOILET.

©1996. Bill Holbrook

SAY, AREN'T YOU THE GIRL MY STEPBROTHER SAW LAST NIGHT?

HI! I'M FIONA! YOU MUST BE LINDESFARNE!

HE CLAIMS YOU PUT A CURSE ON HIM.

YEP! ... CAUSING HIM TO BECOME GENTLE AND COMPASSIONATE AGAINST HIS WILL!

...AND HE BOUGHT IT?

HEY, AS LONG AS THEY CAN BLAME SOMETHING BESIDES THEMSELVES...

©1996. Bill Holbrook

53

55

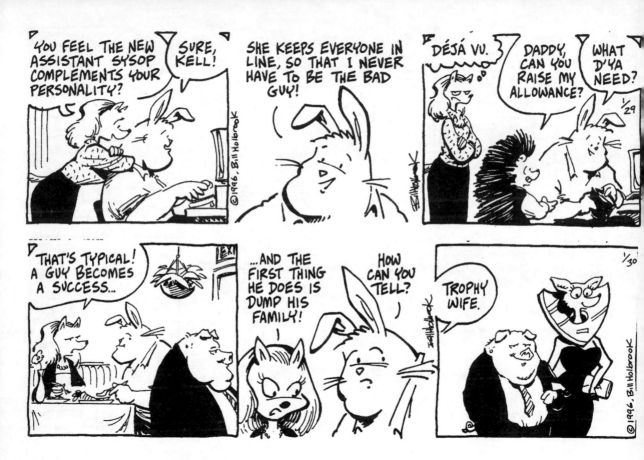

60

61

62

FIONA? IS THAT—?

OH, SURE! A LITTLE MASCARA, AND **NOW** I'M ATTRACTIVE TO YOU?

JUST ANOTHER TYPICAL MALE, HUNG UP ON SUPERFICIAL APPEARANCES!

WHO TOLD YOU **THAT** ABOUT ME?

12/12

© 1996 BillHolbrook

MAKE OVER KIT

FIONA, I DON'T WANT YOU TO THINK I'M HERE JUST BECAUSE YOU GOT A MAKEOVER.

I KNOW, RUDY. YOU LIKED ME BEFORE, BUT COULDN'T ADMIT IT TO YOURSELF.

VALENTINES DANCE

THAT'S WHY YOU IMAGINED THAT SILLY "CURSE" BUSINESS.

I WAS AN IDIOT.

I MEAN, THERE'S NOTHING YOU COULD EVER SAY THAT'D MAKE ME UNHAPPY!

© 1996 BillHolbrook

MY FAMILY'S MOVING IN THE MORNING.

2/13

65

66

SEE, KELL?

LINDESFARNE DOESN'T NEED POISE LESSONS.

I GUESS YOU'RE RIGHT...

© 1996, Bill Holbrook

SHE'S PRETTY GRACEFUL ON THE 'NET.

WATCH ME DANCE AROUND THE ACCESS RESTRICTIONS!

SO THE FOLKS DECIDED YOU DON'T NEED LESSONS IN POISE?

NOPE!

THEY FELT TODAY, ONLINE ETIQUETTE IS MORE IMPORTANT THAN PHYSICAL GRACE OR—

TRIP CRASH

© 1996, Bill Holbrook

OR...?

OH, SHUT UP.

2/23

Bill Holbrook

68

69

70

CANDICE, GET READY FOR A DELUGE OF FOLKS RETURNING TO THE FORUM AFTER A LONG ABSENCE.

WHY, KEVIN?

3/19

BECAUSE OF THE NEW PRICING STRUCTURE? A NEW AD CAMPAIGN? THE GROWING POPULARITY OF THE ONLINE CULTURE?

NAW...

...THEY'RE EMERGING FROM HIBERNATION.

ZZZ :SNORT: GOTTA CHECK E-MAIL... :YAWN:

©1996, Bill Holbrook

THERE'S A LIGHT ON NEXT DOOR AT THE URSALS'.

OH, THEY'RE COMING OUT OF HIBERNATION!

YOU'RE RIGHT! I WONDER WHAT THEY'LL FIND AFTER FIVE MONTHS!

©1996 Bill Holbrook

TECH SUPPORT STILL HAS US ON "HOLD."

5/20

©1996 Bill Holbrook

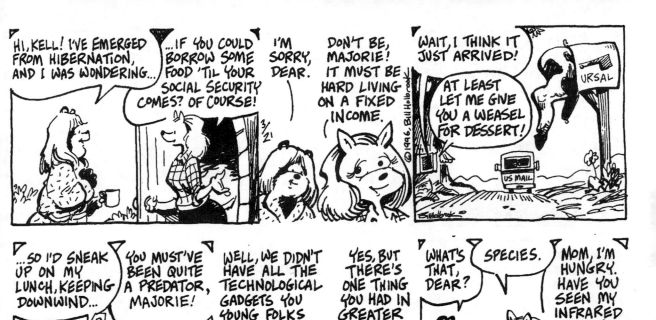

77

78

81

83

84

85

OKAY! GYM CLASS IS OVER! EVERYBODY TAKE A SHOWER!

BOYS GIRLS

© 1996, Bill Holbrook

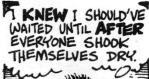

I **KNEW** I SHOULD'VE WAITED UNTIL **AFTER** EVERYONE SHOOK THEMSELVES DRY.

4/18

UGH! MID-APRIL... WHEN TEACHING IS AN ABSOLUTE CHORE! I'M EXHAUSTED!

© 1996, Bill Holbrook

I SWEAR... IF ONE MORE THING HAPPENS...

I ACCIDENTALLY ATE MY OWN HOMEWORK.

SIGH.

FACULTY LOUNGE

4/19

88

89

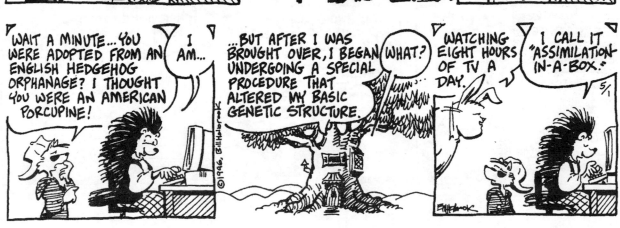

91

93

Panel 1: "LISTEN, I RECHECKED MY DATA, AND I OWE YOU AN APOLOGY... AND A PROMOTION!" "WHAT?!"

Panel 2: "YES, YOUR SECTOR IS ACTUALLY AHEAD OF QUOTA!" "IT IS? OH! OF COURSE IT IS!"

Panel 3: "SO, KELL, WHY DIDN'T YOU TELL ME YOU'D SWITCHED TO SMALL GAME?" "I ... UH... WANTED IT TO BE A SURPRISE!" PTOO! 5/10

Panel 4: "RUDY, IT'S THE END OF THE SCHOOL YEAR. HOW ARE YOUR GRADES?"

Panel 5: "IS MY TUTORING HELPING? ARE YOU GOING TO PASS? ARE YOU BECOMING A PROFICIENT PREDATOR?"

Panel 6: 5/13

96

97

98

WE JOIN OUR INTREPID HEROINE AS SHE EMBARKS ON A JOURNEY ACROSS THE VAST EXPANSE OF THE WORLD WIDE WEB!

©1996, Bill Holbrook

AMID CORPORATE BILLBOARDS AND POINTLESS VANITY PAGES, SHE CONTINUES HER MAGNIFICENT SEARCH! STAY TUNED FOR...

5/22

...*Quest for Content!*

OR, 5,700,000 CHANNELS AND NUTHIN' ON.

DOWNLOADING

DOWNLOADING 32% OF 145K (AT 27 BYTES/SEC.)

DOWNLOAD COMPLETE

5/23

YOU THINK LINDESFARNE IS STAYING UP TOO LATE ON THE 'NET?

IT JUST TAKES HER SO LONG TO GET STARTED IN THE MORNING.

99

101

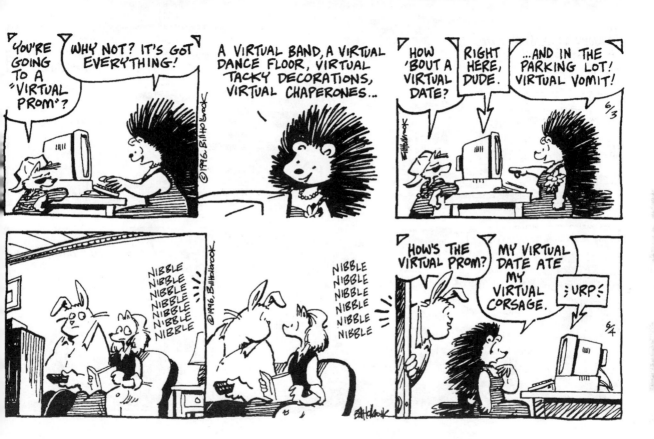

103

"LINDESFARNE, IT'S TIME TO GO TO BED!"

"NO! I'M STILL AT MY VIRTUAL PROM! IT'S NOT OVER! I'M NOT READY TO—"

"HELLO, TECH SUPPORT?"

6/5

"MOM'S GONNA BE IN HER SECRETARY'S WEDDING?"

"YEAH, SHE'S OUT TRYING ON HER BRIDESMAIDS DRESS"

"MY SYMPATHIES."

"THEY'RE ALWAYS EXPENSIVE, AND THE BRIDE TRIES TO JUSTIFY THEM BY CLAIMING THEY'RE SUITABLE FOR OTHER OCCASIONS!"

"TRICK OR TREAT."

"...AND IT COMES WITH A NO-MOLT GUARANTEE!"

6/6

107

"HERE I AM FOR MY FIRST DAY AT THE SUMMER SCHOOL FOR CARNIVORES... WHICH I **KNEW** WOULD BE DOMINATED BY A CERTAIN TYPE."

I JUST HOPE THE MATERIAL HASN'T BEEN TOTALLY GEARED TOWARD THEM!

NOW OUR FIRST LESSON WILL BE ON FINDING THE BEST HONEY...

≥SIGH≥

"CRUMMY SUMMER SCHOOL! A WHOLE VACATION SPENT IN CLASS!"

IS THERE ANYONE ELSE STARING AT SUCH A BORING, DESOLATE THREE MONTHS?

WELCOME TO McROUGHAGE. MAY I TAKE YOUR ORDER PLEASE?

DRIVE-THRU

HOW MUCH JUST TO NIBBLE ON YOUR LANDSCAPING?

108

109

110

111

113

WITH APOLOGIES TO SEGAR, BROWNE, KEANE, YOUNG, GUISEWITE, SCHULZ, JOHNSTON AND GROENING

ANOTHER ROTTEN DAY AT THE McROUGHAGE DRIVE-THRU. SURLY CUSTOMERS, NAGGING BOSSES, ENDLESS HASSLES...

...AND ON TOP OF EVERYTHING ELSE, IT'S RAINING!

UM...THAT **IS** RAIN, ISN'T IT?

CONTINUED!

HELP! I'M ABOUT TO BE EATEN BY COUGARS!

HELP!

GO AHEAD, PORCUPINE! YELL ALL YOU WANT...

NO ONE CAN HEAR YOU!

BABY MONITOR

117

119

120

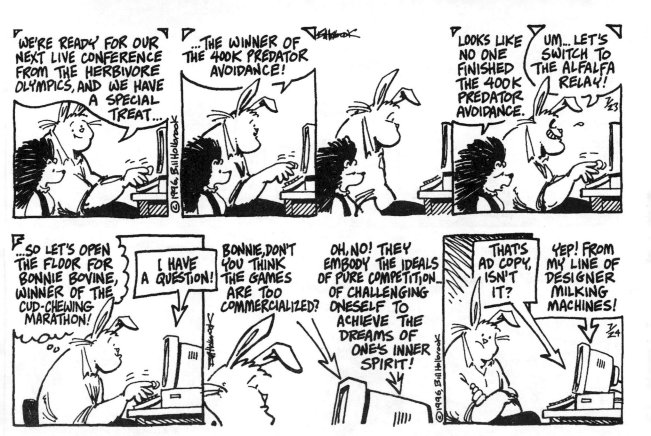

121

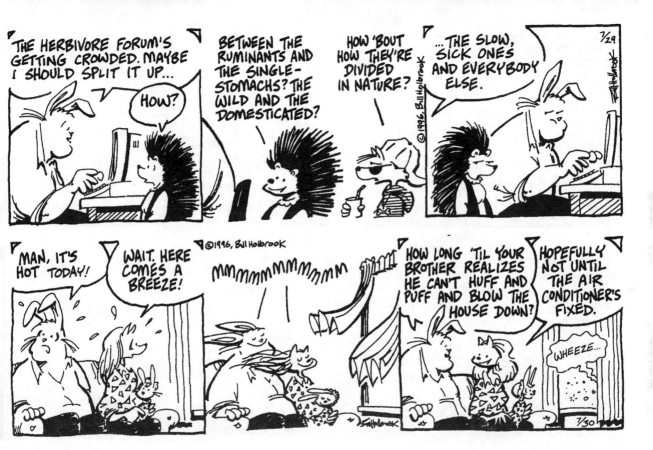

123

126

127

129

131

134

135

137

138

139